presents

Family Bible Classics

ISBN - 1-60143-420-0

Contents

Dear Parents,

Welcome to the *Hooked on Phonics® Presents Family Bible Classics*, a beautifully bound volume including some of the best loved stories of the Bible. Introduce your child to the amazing stories of the Old and New Testament with easy-to-understand language and rich, memorable illustrations.

To make the most out of your experience with this outstanding collection:

Stimulate your child's thinking about the Bible.
Use the Bible Lesson and Discussion Questions that follow the stories to engage your child in conversation about the Bible stories. Encourage him to relate the stories and lessons to his own life.

Introduce new words.
When you encounter a word that is unfamiliar to your child, refer to the Glossary in the back of the book to help explain its meaning.

Get the whole family involved.
Read the Bible stories together. These stories are rich with content that is sure to engage the entire family. Read the books together.

Enjoy these *Family Bible Classics*!

Introduction to the Bible

The Bible is an amazing book. The separate books of the Bible were written by many different people at many different times. All told, the Bible was written over a period of one thousand years.

Sometimes the Bible is called by different names. Some people call it the Holy Bible, others the Word of God, and some call it the Scriptures. The Bible is separated into two different sections—the Old Testament, which tells of God's covenant with the Israelites, and the New Testament, which tells of the life of Jesus and the history of the beginning of God's church.

The Old Testament is made up of 39 different kinds of books. There are books about God's laws, books about history, books that are filled with poetry and songs, and books full of stories about the creation of the world and God's relationship with humankind. Some of the best known people in the Old Testament are Adam and Eve, Noah, Joseph, Moses, David, Daniel, and Jonah.

The New Testament is made up of 27 different books that tell of the life of Jesus, His teachings, and the history of the beginning of God's church. It includes four Gospels, the book of Acts, 21 letters written by different people, and the last book in the Bible, Revelation.

Old Testament

In the Beginning

Retold by
Karen Baicker

Illustrated by
Kristina Swarner

Genesis 1:1–3:24

This is the story of how God created Heaven and Earth. It also tells of the first two people, Adam and Eve, and how, after a taste of the fruit from the Tree of Knowledge, God threw them out of the Garden of Eden.

In the beginning, there was no Earth. Imagine there were no animals, no plants, and no people. There were no rocks or air or stars. There was nothing but God. This is the story of how God created Heaven and Earth, and how the world began.

In the beginning, the world was an endless, dark, shapeless ocean. God hovered over this darkness and said, "Let there be light." And when He spoke these words, there was light! And God saw that it was good.

Then God separated the light from the darkness. He called the light "day" and the darkness "night." Together, the light and the darkness became the first day. And God saw again that it was good.

On the second day, the world was still only water. So God said, "Let there be space between the waters above and the waters below." Then the sky appeared, and Heaven and Earth were created. And God saw again that it was good.

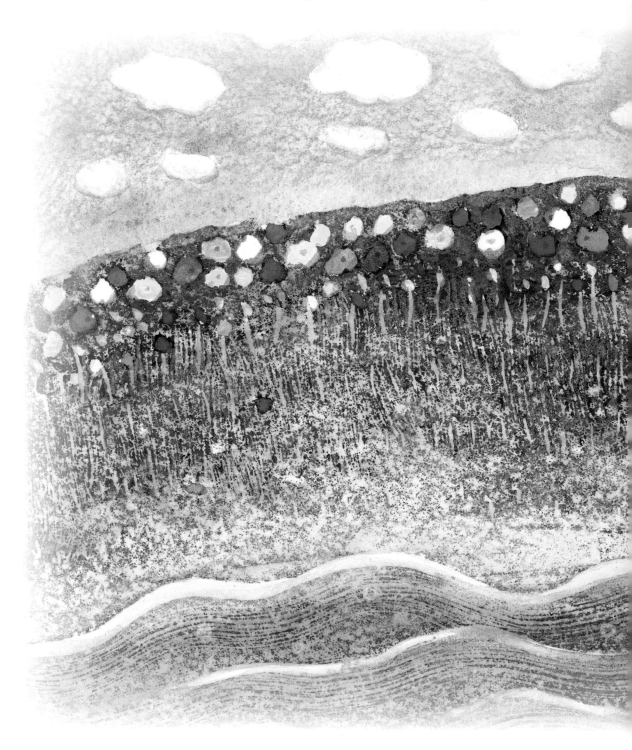

On the third day, God spoke again. "Let the waters beneath the sky gather into one place, so that dry ground appears." God named the dry ground "land" and the water "seas." He filled the Earth with plants and saw again that it was good.

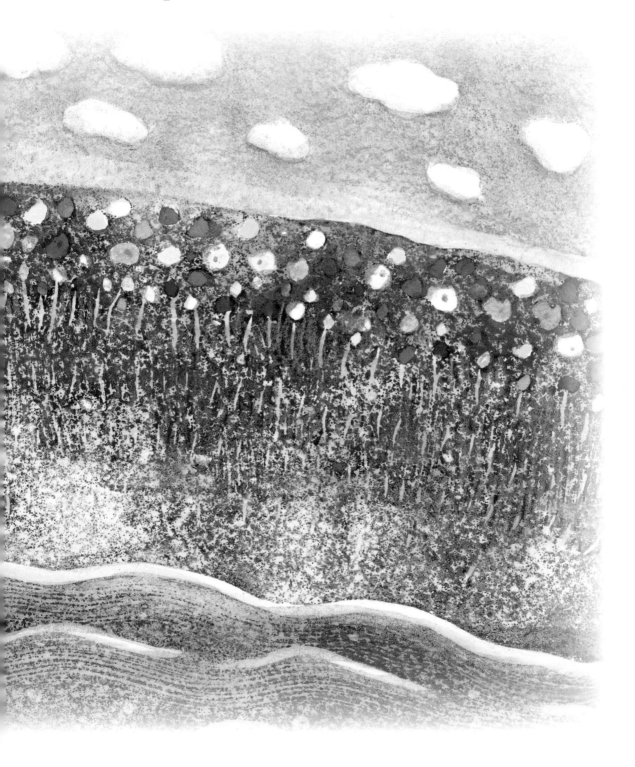

On the fourth day, God said, "Let bright lights appear in the sky at night. Let these lights shine down on the Earth." He created the sun, moon, and stars to guide the days and nights. The sun brightened the day. The moon lit the Earth at night. The stars twinkled in the night sky. Planets circled the heavens. God set everything in motion to create seasons and measure time.

11

On the fifth day, God filled the Earth with life. He said, "Let the seas swarm with fish and other life. Let the skies be filled with birds of every kind."

Suddenly the seas were filled with fish, crabs, and whales. The skies were singing with robins, bluebirds, and eagles.

On the sixth day, God said, "Let the Earth give us every kind of animal," and soon there were cows, lions, grasshoppers, and fleas.

God still needed someone to care for the plants and animals. He gathered some dust and breathed life into it. And that's how the first man, Adam, was made.

On the seventh day, God told Adam, "Look at this beautiful world!"

God had created the world, and He saw that it was good. He blessed the seventh day, called the Sabbath, and rested from the hard work of His creation.

God made a beautiful garden, called Eden, for Adam. He said, "Take good care of this garden. You can eat anything that grows here. The only fruit you must never eat is from the special Tree of Knowledge. If you eat its fruit, you will die."

God brought animals for Adam to name. He brought an animal with a long neck, and Adam called it a "giraffe." He brought an animal with a baby pouch, and Adam called it a "kangaroo." Each animal had its own special beauty, and Adam was happy.

Still, God could see that Adam was lonely. God said, "I will make someone for Adam to love." That night, while Adam slept deeply, God took a rib from Adam's chest, and breathed life into it. And that's how the first woman, Eve, was born.

When Adam awoke, he saw Eve sleeping next to him. Birds were singing and flowers were blooming, and Adam rejoiced.

Adam was no longer alone in the garden. Together, Adam and Eve lived in peace with the animals around them. Everything they needed was provided for by God. God was good!

Then a snake entered the garden. He was
clever, sneaky, and up to no good.

One day he hissed, "Why don't you try
one of these delicious fruits?" And he nodded
toward the ripe fruit hanging from the Tree of
Knowledge.

At first Eve said no, but the snake convinced her that one little bite wouldn't hurt. It was so delicious! Eve wanted to share the fruit with Adam, and he tasted it, too.

Adam and Eve knew they'd made a terrible mistake. God had asked only one thing of them, and they had let Him down! What could they do?

They hid among the leafy trees. Adam heard God calling out to him, so he stepped forward. "You have eaten from the Tree of Knowledge," God said.

Adam pointed to Eve and said, "She brought me the fruit!"

Eve pointed to the snake and cried, "He tricked me into eating it!"

23

Angrily God cursed the snake. "You will crawl on your belly and eat dust for the rest of your life."

Then he turned to Adam and Eve. "You have disobeyed me. You must leave this lovely garden. You will face many challenges, and one day you will die."

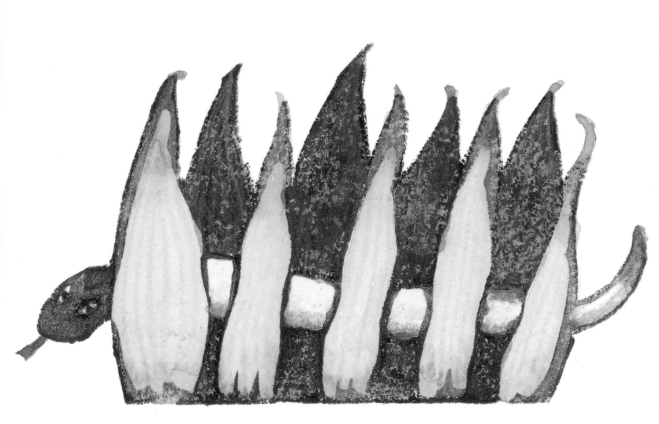

Sadly they stepped out into the world. Life was no longer easy, but they knew that God still cared about them and always would.

Bible Lesson

God has told us that He created everything that exists. God created the first two people, Adam and Eve. Adam and Eve disobeyed God and were punished. When we do something that God tells us is wrong, it is called a sin.

Discussion Questions

The Earth is God's amazing creation. What are different ways that you can take care of it? How do you take care of plants? Animals? Other people?

God rested on the seventh day, after six days of hard work. What does your family do on days of rest after a week of work and school?

Have you ever wanted to blame someone else when you made a bad choice and got in trouble? Why is it important to tell the truth?

Noah's Ark

Retold by
Zoë Kashner

Illustrated by
Kathy Mitchell

Genesis 6:1–9:17

When God sent a huge flood
to wash over the entire Earth,
He asked a very good man
named Noah to build a huge
boat and save all the animals.

Noah was a good man who lived a long time ago. God asked him to do something special—to save his family and the animals of the world. Noah had to show patience, hard work, and courage.

Noah lived with his family. God knew they were good people. But other people in the world were not good like Noah.

God told Noah there would be a huge flood.

The rain would fall and the oceans would rise.
All of the Earth would be covered in water.
God told Noah that he would be kept safe, but
only if he did what God told him to do.

God told Noah to build a huge boat called an ark. The ark would need to fit Noah and his family and two of every animal in the world. Noah and his sons worked hard to build the ark, and finally it was done.

As Noah sat in the ark, the animals came two at a time, from the tiniest mouse to the largest elephant.

Two donkeys…

…two giraffes…

…two oxen…

…two cats…

...two pigs...

...two horses...

...two dogs...

...two foxes...

…and every other kind of animal in the whole world walked onto the ark. Noah wasn't sure if they all would fit, but whenever two more would arrive, the other animals made room. Just when he thought all of the animals had arrived, along came two of every kind of bird!

Once every animal was on the ark, the wind started to blow, and the rain started to fall. God told Noah it was time to shut the ark and prepare for the flood.

God said, "For forty days and forty nights, the rain will not end."

The rain poured down. It rained and rained. The oceans rose up, with wave after wave covering the land.

At first, the waves were wild, and the ark rocked back and forth. Even the highest mountains were covered with water.

Noah's family waited patiently. The animals waited patiently. Everyone tried not to fight or squirm. They all knew they would be in the boat for a very, very long time.

Finally the rain stopped. The water slowly began to get lower and lower, and the ark came to rest on top of a mountain. Noah opened a window and watched as the water continued to go down.

Noah wanted to make sure it was safe to go outside. He sent a dove to look for dry land. The dove returned, and Noah knew it had not found dry land.

Seven days later Noah sent the dove out again. When the dove returned, it was carrying an olive branch in its beak! Noah now knew there must be trees above the water at last.

A week later Noah sent the dove out again, and this time it didn't come back. Noah knew the dove had found a home and that the Earth was safe and dry.

It was time for the animals to be let out of the ark! Noah walked out onto the land with all of the pairs of animals…

…cats and foxes…

…pigs and horses…

…and birds flying all around.

Once all of the animals had left the ark, they gathered around Noah, and he began to pray. He thanked God that the Earth was dry again and that his family was safe.

God promised He would never send a flood to cover the Earth again.

As a sign of His promise, God created the first rainbow. It filled the whole sky with color.

Bible Lesson

Noah did what was right and pleasing to God in a time when other people did not. Noah obeyed God's directions to build the ark, knowing that God would bring the flood as He said He would.

Discussion Questions

What do you think other people thought of Noah when he was building such a huge boat? Do you think it was hard for him to do something that others might not understand or make fun of?

Noah, his family, and all of the animals were squeezed into the ark for a very long time! What do you think it would have been like to be on the ark? Why do you think everyone on the boat needed to be patient? Have you ever had to be patient while going somewhere with other people?

God showed Noah a rainbow so we could remember His promise, and God never breaks His promises. Have you ever made a promise that you didn't keep, or did someone break his promise to you?

Joseph the Dreamer

Retold by
Zoë Kashner

Illustrated by
Kate Hosford

Genesis 37:1–45:28

This is the story of a man named Joseph. Terrible things happened to Joseph, but God had a plan for him, and Joseph became a great leader in Egypt.

Joseph was his father Jacob's favorite son. He had eleven brothers—ten older brothers and one baby brother, Benjamin.

One day Jacob gave Joseph a present. It was a beautiful coat of many colors. Jacob had no presents for Joseph's brothers, and the older brothers were jealous and began to hate Joseph.

Joseph had an amazing dream one night, and he told his brothers about it. "There we were in the fields," he explained. "My bundle of wheat stood upright. Then your bundles of wheat bowed to mine."

His brothers asked angrily, "Do you think you will be our ruler?"

Joseph had a second dream. "The sun, the moon, and the stars bowed down to me," he told his family.

"Joseph, are you saying that your whole family should bow before you?" asked his father.

Everyone but Joseph was troubled by the dream.

One afternoon Jacob sent Joseph to check on his brothers in the fields. Joseph wore his beautiful coat of many colors. When father and son said goodbye, neither knew that it was the last time they would see each other for many years.

Joseph's brothers had a plan.
    When Joseph joined them, they took his coat
and then sold him to some slave traders who
were passing by.

To fool their father, they dipped Joseph's coat in sheep's blood and claimed that Joseph had been killed by a wild animal. Jacob was heartbroken.

Across a huge desert, in the land of Egypt,
Joseph wasn't dead. He was the servant of a man
in the court of Pharaoh, the king of Egypt. But
the mean wife of Joseph's owner sent Joseph to
prison.

In prison Joseph met two men. One had been the pharaoh's cup bearer. The other had been the pharaoh's baker. They told Joseph their dreams.

The cup bearer said, "In my dream I pressed grapes into juice, which I gave to Pharaoh."

Joseph said, "Great news! You will get your old job back!"

The baker said, "In my dream, I had a breadbasket. But birds came and ate all of the bread."

"Bad news," Joseph said. "You won't get your old job back."

Both dreams came true. Joseph had an amazing gift—he could tell the meaning of dreams.

Pharaoh was having dreams of his own.
First, seven skinny cows came and ate seven healthy cows. Then, seven tiny ears of corn swallowed up seven big ears of corn.

Pharaoh's cup bearer remembered Joseph from prison and said that only Joseph could tell what the dreams meant. Pharaoh freed Joseph from prison and brought him to his palace.

"You will have seven years of plenty, followed by seven years with no food," Joseph explained to Pharaoh.

Pharoah was impressed with Joseph. He said, "From now on you are in charge. Make sure that we save enough to survive the years with no food."

Joseph traveled around Egypt storing grain. After Pharaoh, he was the most important person in Egypt. He had a grand palace of his own. He had a wife and children. No one could tell that he had been born in a land far away. He didn't look like someone who had been a slave.

Seven years of plenty passed.

Then famine came.
Stalks of corn withered.
Cows starved.
But because of Joseph's planning, the
Egyptians had plenty to eat.

In Joseph's homeland, his own father and brothers had no food.

Leaving young Benjamin at home, the brothers went to Egypt to beg for grain. They didn't recognize Joseph now that he was a great man. But Joseph knew them right away and was still angry about what they had done to him.

"You are spies," he told his brothers.

"No," they said, "we were just twelve brothers. One is dead. The other is at home with our father."

"Prove it," said Joseph. "Bring me your other brother."

Thinking they were being punished for what they had done to Joseph, the brothers went home to fetch Benjamin.

When the brothers returned, Joseph saw his little brother and was overcome with happiness. He cried, but he hid his tears.

A lunch was served for all of the brothers. While they ate, Joseph told his servants, "Take this goblet, and put it in Benjamin's bag. Then after the brothers leave, catch them and bring Benjamin back to me."

The servants did as they were told. The brothers left and then were dragged back to Joseph.

Joseph pulled the goblet from Benjamin's bag. "Benjamin is a thief," he said. "He will have to stay here."

"Please," said his brother Judah, "take me instead. My father has already lost his favorite son Joseph. If you take his next favorite, it will break his heart."

Joseph started crying. He could see that his older brothers had changed, and he forgave them. Finally, he spoke.

"I am Joseph," he said.

His brothers gasped with surprise. Joseph hugged his brothers.

Jacob was overjoyed to hear the news. "My son Joseph is alive!" he cried.

That night God came to Jacob in a dream. He said, "Go down to Egypt. There I will make of you and your sons a great nation."

Joseph's brothers brought their father and their own families back to Egypt and settled there. It was just like in Joseph's childhood dreams about stars and wheat. All of Egypt—and all of his family—were protected by him as their leader.

Bible Lesson

God had a special plan for Joseph's life. Even though Joseph had some bad things happen to him, God worked everything out to fulfill His purpose for Joseph.

Discussion Questions

Joseph's brothers were jealous when their father gave Joseph the beautiful coat, and that made them do terrible things to Joseph. Why is it bad to be jealous?

Joseph was able to forgive his brothers for what they had done to him. Why is it important to forgive people, especially if they are sorry for what they've done?

Talk about what a famine is and how to help other people if they are in need of anything.

Moses and the Ten Commandments

Retold by
Julie Stiegemeyer

Illustrated by
Jennifer Hayden

Exodus 19:1–20:21

Read about Moses, a man who
was chosen by God to lead the
Israelites out of slavery in Egypt
and to tell the people His rules,
by which they should live.

Long ago a man named Moses lived in the land of Egypt. God cared for Moses and protected him from the time that he was a little baby. God had a special job for Moses to do.

God's people, the Israelites, worked
and worked under the hot sun as slaves in
Egypt. Their work was never done, and
their masters were cruel, so God chose
Moses to lead His people to the Promised
Land. God parted the Red Sea, and Moses
and the Israelites walked through the sea on
dry land. God saved them! Moses and all of
the people praised God.

But God's people hadn't made it to the Promised Land yet. God cared for His people as they wandered in the desert. The Promised Land was far away, and the Israelites were hungry, so God gave them food and drink and all they needed.

77

The Israelites knew that God would continue to care for them, even in the wilderness. But they needed to learn how God wanted them to love Him and care for each other. Soon they came to a big mountain called Mount Sinai.

God came down to the top of the mountain in fire, wrapping Mount Sinai in a cloud of smoke.

Lightning flashed and trumpets blared louder and louder. The whole mountain shook, and the people were frightened.

Moses, God's messenger, would help the people know God.

The mountain was trembling, lightning was flashing, and thunder was crashing, but Moses went up to the top of the mountain to talk with God.

God spoke to Moses in thunder. God wanted everyone to know His laws, so He gave Moses these commandments on two stone tablets to take down to the people.

First the commandments told how people should love God. God said we should worship and serve Him alone and make no false gods.

God also said we should not curse or lie using His name, but that we should honor and love Him more than anything or anyone else. Then God said to remember the Sabbath day by keeping it holy.

God also taught about families. Each child must honor his father and mother, and husbands and wives should love and be faithful to each other.

God said that it is wrong to murder, and that we should not take things that belong to others.

God commanded that we not lie about other people. He also said we should not covet, or want things that belong to other people.

Moses came down from the mountain and told the people what God had said. He reminded them that they were already God's people. He told them God's laws and how to love God and serve each other. Moses was a great prophet, helping the people know God and His commandments.

And God continued to love and care for His people as they traveled to the Promised Land and beyond.

Bible Lesson

When Moses traveled with the Israelites, God gave them new rules to follow so they would know how to live in a way that was pleasing to Him. God wanted them to be good because they were His special people.

Discussion Questions

God chose Moses to do some very important things. Talk about Moses' journey leading the Israelites from Egypt to Mount Sinai. What makes a great leader?

Why is it important to follow rules? What would happen if people didn't obey traffic lights? What other rules are there for our benefit?

How do wrong actions affect other people? How do you feel if someone does something bad to you?

David and Goliath

Retold by
Alison Blank

Illustrated by
Bryan Langdo

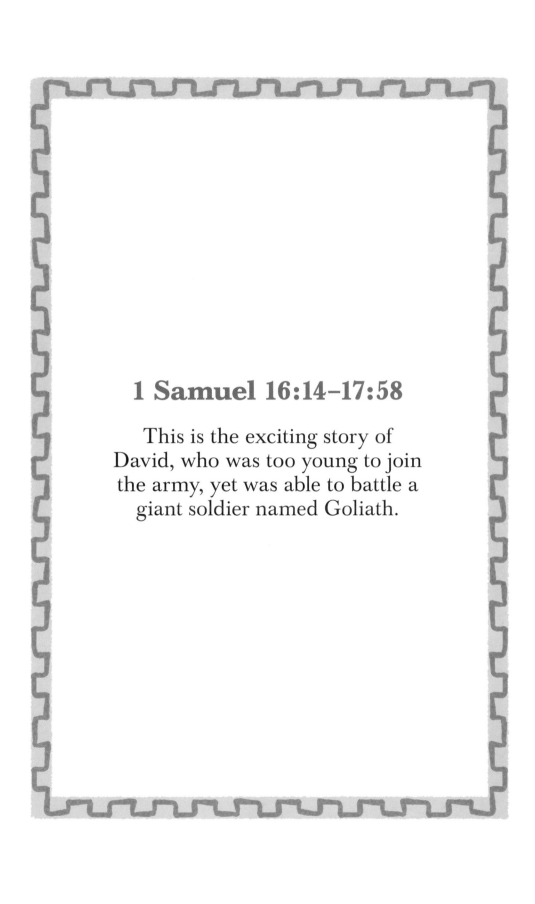

1 Samuel 16:14–17:58

This is the exciting story of David, who was too young to join the army, yet was able to battle a giant soldier named Goliath.

David was the youngest of eight sons. He was a handsome boy who took care of the family's sheep. He spent his days in the rolling hills, making sure the sheep were safe and well cared for.

Just as David was good at tending sheep, he was also good at playing a harp. He could pluck melodies so beautiful that the sheep in the fields would stop to listen.

King Saul, the king of the Israelites, heard of David's music and asked the boy to come play for him. David's melodies soothed the troubled king. From then on, David traveled back and forth to play for King Saul and care for his father's sheep.

Not long after, King Saul's army began to prepare for war against the Philistines. David wanted to join the army, but he was too young. David's brothers were old enough, so they set out to join the other soldiers in the Valley of Elah.

David's father worried about his sons. He asked David to go after them, bring them food, and make sure they were safe.

When David arrived, he saw the two great armies preparing for battle. On one side stood the Israelites. On the other side stood the Philistines. Each army formed a line that stretched as far as the eye could see.

Before David had a chance to greet his brothers, the enemy line parted, and a soldier stepped forward. But this was not an ordinary soldier. This was a fierce-looking giant! David could not believe his eyes.

This terrifying giant named Goliath was as tall as four men standing one on top of another. Each day Goliath stepped forward and spoke the same words to the Israelites.

"Is there one man among you who will come forward and fight me? If you can kill me, we'll become your servants. But if I kill you, your soldiers will become our servants."

As the soldiers trembled with fear, David asked loudly, "Why doesn't anyone fight him?"

Suddenly David's brothers felt embarrassed. Then they grew angry. "Why are you here?" they asked. "Why aren't you home taking care of the sheep?"

But David continued, "If no one else will fight him, I will!"

"You are too young," said his brothers.

"You are a musician, not a soldier," said King Saul. "You don't have enough experience to fight this Philistine."

David replied, "All these years I have kept the sheep safe from lions and bears that have tried to kill them. God will give me courage. If I can face wild animals, I can face this giant." David insisted so strongly that King Saul finally agreed.

"If you are going to fight the giant, you must have a sword and armor like his," said King Saul. He helped David put on a magnificent suit of armor. But the armor was too big and heavy, and David took it off.

Nearby was a stream, and David reached
down into the clear water. He pulled out one
smooth stone, and then another, until he had five
in all. He had all that he needed—his slingshot,
five stones, and God by his side.

As David neared Goliath, the giant took a step forward and laughed. His laughter echoed throughout the valley.

Goliath said, "All you've brought are sticks? Am I supposed to run and fetch them like some dog? Surely you need more than sticks and stones to fight a great warrior like me!"

"I have all I need," said David. Then he took a round stone from his pocket, placed it carefully in his slingshot, and pulled it back. There was silence as David let go.

The stone sailed through the air. It hit Goliath squarely in the middle of his forehead. And with a huge thud that shook the entire valley, Goliath fell to the ground in a cloud of dust.

With Goliath's great fall, King Saul's soldiers shouted and cheered. The war was over before it had begun. The sounds of celebration rang from every hill and valley in the kingdom. Brave young David had killed the mighty giant in one blow.

Bible Lesson

Because David trusted in God's strength and help, he knew that he would win the battle against Goliath.

Discussion Questions

David was a young boy when he fought Goliath. He didn't wear armor and had only a slingshot. Why wasn't he afraid?

Remember that each fear is like a "Goliath" and that God will help you overcome your fears. What kinds of things are you afraid of? What can you do to help yourself triumph over them?

David's music soothed King Saul when he was troubled. What soothes you when you're troubled?

Daniel
in the
Lions' Den

Retold by
Alison Blank

Illustrated by
Melissa Iwai

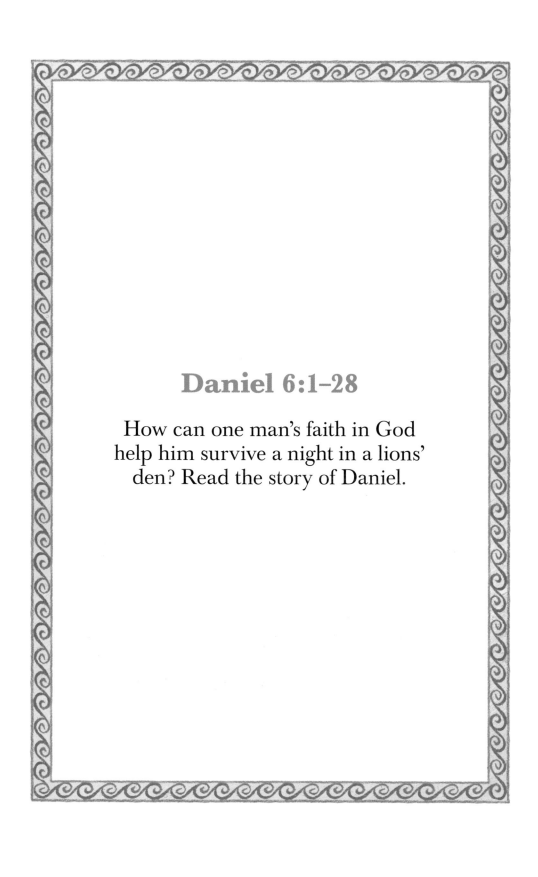

Daniel 6:1–28

How can one man's faith in God
help him survive a night in a lions'
den? Read the story of Daniel.

As a young boy in Jerusalem, Daniel was taught by his parents to pray to God every day. Later, even when Daniel was captured and brought to Babylon, he never stopped praying.

Daniel grew up to be smart and wise. He proved to be so smart and wise that Darius, the new king of Babylon, asked Daniel to become one of his advisors to help him rule his kingdom. Daniel felt honored.

Daniel worked very hard and did very well. King Darius was pleased and put him in charge of all of the advisors.

The other advisors were jealous. "Why didn't the king choose one of us?" they wanted to know. The more the men thought about it, the angrier they became. They decided they'd have to get Daniel in trouble with the king. But how?

The men watched Daniel day and night, hoping to catch him doing something wrong. But he didn't do anything wrong. Daniel was simply a good man who prayed to God every day.

Finally the men had an idea! They said to the king, "You are great and powerful. You should have a new law that says people must pray only to you. Anyone who disobeys will be thrown to the lions."

King Darius was flattered and quickly agreed.

Daniel heard about the law, and he knew he couldn't obey it. He loved his God too much. The men spied on Daniel to find out what he'd do. He did just what they had hoped. Daniel got down on his knees and prayed to God. They raced back to the king to tell on Daniel.

When King Darius heard the news, he was heartsick. What had he done? The king didn't want to arrest Daniel, but the men all said that the law was the law.

King Darius ordered his soldiers to take Daniel to the lions. The soldiers kicked down Daniel's door. Daniel didn't put up a fight as they led him away.

The king watched as the soldiers threw Daniel into the lions' den. He saw Daniel fold his hands in prayer and heard the lions growl as the door slammed shut. Then the soldiers pushed a huge stone into place to block the door.

"May your God save you," King Darius whispered.

All night long the king tossed and turned. He shut his eyes tight, but he still saw the lions' sharp teeth. He held his hands over his ears, but he still heard their roars.

Finally morning came. The first rays of sun lit the king's bedroom. Already dressed, King Darius jumped up and raced to the lions' den.

"Daniel! Can you hear me? Are you all right?"
King Darius shouted through the door. "Did your
God save you from the lions?" He was afraid
there would be no answer.

But King Darius didn't hear lions. Instead he heard a quiet voice from inside the den. The voice said, "It is Daniel. I am alive."

The king was overjoyed. At his order, the soldiers rolled away the stone. The door opened and there stood Daniel with not a mark on him.

"How did you survive?" King Darius asked.
Daniel said calmly, "God knew I hadn't done anything wrong. He sent a guardian angel to protect me. It was the angel who shut the lions' mouths so they couldn't hurt me."

King Darius immediately ordered the men
who had plotted against Daniel brought to him.
"Throw them to the lions," he told the soldiers.
Everyone heard the hungry lions roar.

King Darius was so amazed by what he had
seen that he made a new law. This new law said
that the whole kingdom should worship the God
who had saved Daniel from the lions.

Bible Lesson

Daniel loved, worshipped, and prayed to God, even when people told him he couldn't.

Discussion Questions

Daniel knew he was breaking the law when he continued to pray to God. Was he wrong for breaking the law?

What did King Darius learn about God from Daniel?

God sent a guardian angel to protect Daniel. Are there times when you need a guardian angel?

Jonah
and the
Whale

Retold by
Zoë Kashner

Illustrated by
Phyllis Harris

Jonah 1:1–4:11

This is the story of Jonah,
who tried to disobey God but got
a second chance inside the belly
of a whale.

One day God told Jonah, "Get up and go to the city of Nineveh. Tell the people there to change their bad ways."

Jonah had heard of Nineveh. It was a huge and busy city in a land far away.

Jonah didn't want to go because he thought people in Nineveh were bad and needed to be punished. But God had told him to go. Jonah had always been good at hiding. He decided it was time to hide from God.

He found a ship leaving for a town in a different direction. God would never find him there, he thought. He paid the sailors to take him aboard.

Once the ship was at sea,
God created a huge storm around it.
Heavy waves crashed across the ship's deck.

First the sailors tried to lighten the load. They tossed cargo into the sea. Then the sailors began to pray to their gods. Everyone prayed except

Jonah. The captain noticed that he had actually
fallen asleep, curled up in the ship's hold.

"What is the matter with you?" the captain
asked. "Why aren't you praying?"

Jonah didn't answer.

The sailors decided to cast lots to find out who was causing the storm. The lots said it was Jonah. All of the sailors stared at him as the wind and waves crashed on the ship.

"What have you done to cause this?" asked a sailor.

Jonah explained that he was running away from God.

The sea became even stormier.

Another sailor asked, "What should we do to calm the storm?"

"You have to throw me overboard," said Jonah sadly.

At first the sailors didn't want to throw Jonah overboard. They rowed as hard as they could for dry land, but the storm swirled around them and beat their boat against the waves. Finally, together they picked up Jonah and dropped him into the sea.

The storm calmed right away. The clouds cleared. The bright sun shone above. The sailors sadly rowed along their way while Jonah sank beneath the waves.

Jonah sank down into the dark sea. He felt certain he would die, and he closed his eyes.

When he opened his eyes again, he seemed to be in a damp cave. He could hear a loud *thump*, *thump*, *thump*, like an enormous

heartbeat. Just then a rush of water knocked
him off his feet. He held onto a barnacle as a
school of minnows swam past him.

All of a sudden Jonah realized where he
was. He was trapped in the belly of a whale.

Jonah thanked God for sparing his life. Jonah knew He was giving him a second chance.

"Dear God," he prayed. "I will do what you've asked me to do. Please let me out of this whale's belly."

For three days and three nights, Jonah prayed
to God. He wondered if he would ever see his
home again. He felt bad for disobeying God
and running away. Finally his prayers were
answered. Jonah was spit ashore by the whale.

Jonah dried himself off and set out on the road to Nineveh.

He was scared by the crowded streets of Nineveh, but he knew what he had to do. He walked around shouting, "Repent! Repent! You have forty days to repent or God will destroy Nineveh."

To Jonah's surprise, people paid attention. Little children tugged on their parents' sleeves and stopped to stare and listen. Workers put down their tools and scratched their chins thoughtfully. The king's messenger heard Jonah's message and ran up the path to the palace.

Everyone in Nineveh repented. Even the king took off his rich clothes.

God was pleased and decided not to destroy the city after all. The people of Nineveh celebrated. Only Jonah was unhappy.

"God, I'm so mad at you!" he shouted. "Why would you want to save these bad people?"

He ran out of the city and built a small hut where he sat by himself.

Jonah was very uncomfortable in his hut. The sun baked through the roof and made his head feel hot enough to melt.

Then overnight, God grew a tree that completely covered Jonah's hut. The tree had a

wonderfully cool shade. When Jonah woke up, he felt relaxed and happy.

Jonah spent the day whistling and daydreaming. He fell asleep by the lullaby of the breeze through the branches of the tree.

The next morning Jonah woke up to the hot sun on his head. He saw the tree dead on the ground. With tears pouring down his face, Jonah said, "I can't believe you killed this beautiful tree!"

God said, "You are upset about a single tree. Think of my feeling for Nineveh. Why shouldn't I love the people and animals there?"

Jonah thought about what God had said. God had given him a second chance when he prayed in the belly of the whale. Maybe the people of Nineveh deserved a second chance as well.

Bible Lesson

After trying to hide from God, Jonah discovered that it is important to always obey God. God gave Jonah a second chance by sending a whale, helping Jonah learn to obey Him.

Discussion Questions

How did Jonah feel about going to Nineveh? Have you ever had to do something you did not want to, but knew you had to?

God gave Jonah a second chance to obey Him by sending a whale. Why are second chances important?

How did Jonah feel when the tree died? What was God trying to explain to him about saving Nineveh?

New Testament

When Jesus Was Born

Retold by
Zoë Kashner

Illustrated by
Kathy Mitchell

Luke 2:1–20

This is the amazing story of how
a baby named Jesus was born to
Mary and Joseph in a stable
in Bethlehem.

A long time ago there was a young woman named Mary. She lived with her parents in a town called Nazareth. She was kind, hardworking, and faithful, and she was planning to marry a carpenter named Joseph.

One day, Mary was sitting quietly by herself after finishing her chores. Suddenly an angel appeared! He was the angel Gabriel, God's messenger. At first Mary was scared. Nothing like this had ever happened to her before.

"Don't be afraid, Mary," Gabriel said. "God has chosen you for a special life. You are blessed. I have come to tell you that you are going to have a son. Your son will be the Savior, the hope of all people. You shall call him Jesus. He will be the Son of God."

Mary and Joseph watched in wonder as Mary's belly grew. They began to prepare for the birth of the baby.

A few months later, the emperor who ruled the land decided to count all of the people in his kingdom. Joseph and Mary had to return to the town where Joseph was born.

Joseph's family was part of the House of David. They were from Bethlehem. Mary and Joseph packed their belongings and prepared for the journey.

All over the land, families prepared to move back to the towns where the head of each household had been born. They packed food and water, blankets and clothing. They traveled however they could. Some rode donkeys. Others had to walk.

Joseph and Mary left Nazareth. Their journey was long and tiring. Joseph led a donkey that Mary rode. They hoped they would make it to Bethlehem before the baby was born.

Joseph and Mary finally arrived in Bethlehem. They looked for somewhere to stay, but no one had room for them. Joseph knocked on almost every door in town.

Finally, a kind innkeeper felt sorry for them. He saw that Mary was about to have a baby. All of his rooms were full, so he showed the couple to a warm stable where he kept his animals. Joseph made Mary a comfortable bed in the straw.

That night the baby boy was born. As stars lit up the sky Mary wrapped him in soft cloths and laid him in a manger. Just like the angel Gabriel had told her to do, she named the baby Jesus.

It was a miracle—the Son of God was born!
Mary and Joseph looked at the holy child
in wonder.

Everyone in Bethlehem was sleeping. Just outside of town, there were a few young shepherds watching their flock in the countryside. Suddenly the shepherds saw an angel coming down out of the stars of the dark night sky. At first they were scared, but then the angel spoke.

"I have come to tell you news of great joy!" the angel said. "The Son of God has been born tonight. He is sleeping in a manger in Bethlehem."

The shepherds were overjoyed. When the angel left, they decided to go to see the baby with their own eyes. They raced through the fields and into the town. They ran down the quiet village streets until they found the quiet stable next to the inn. A small light shone from inside.

Mary and Joseph welcomed the shepherds.
They all looked at Jesus with wonder. He was the
Son of God!

The shepherds wanted to share the good news with the whole world. They bid Mary, Joseph, and the baby Jesus goodbye.

As they ran through the streets of Bethlehem, they shouted to everyone they met, "The Savior is born! Jesus, Son of God, has been born this day."

Bible Lesson

God made a promise a long time ago that He would send His Son to be the hope of all people. Jesus is God's Son, the promised Savior.

Discussion Questions

Everyone likes to get good news! What good news did the angel Gabriel bring to Mary? Did the good news come true?

What was it like for Mary and Joseph to get ready for Jesus' birth? How do you think they felt about having such a big responsibility?

Why were the shepherds overjoyed when they heard that Jesus was born? What did they do when the angel told them the news? How do you celebrate Jesus' birth?

Five Loaves
and Two Fish

Retold by
Julie Stiegemeyer

Illustrated by
Nicole Tadgell

Matthew 14:13–21, Mark 6:30–44, Luke 9:10–17, John 6:1–15

Read this miraculous tale of a time when Jesus took five loaves and two fish and made a meal that fed thousands of people.

ong ago, Jesus walked and talked with the people, teaching them about the kingdom of God. He told them of God's love. He healed their sicknesses. He helped them as only He could.

Once, after a long day of teaching, Jesus was tired. He wanted to find a place to rest.

Jesus sailed across the Sea of Galilee to a quiet spot where He could be alone with His Disciples, His twelve closest followers.

But a large crowd sailed across the water too. They wanted to be near Jesus. They wanted Jesus to teach them. They wanted Him to heal them. They wanted Him to help them as only He could.

Even more people came to see Jesus. The crowd grew and grew.

Jesus looked out on the crowd of people and loved them. They were like sheep without a shepherd.

Even though Jesus was tired, He taught the people who gathered around Him. He told them about God's love. He told them how to help their neighbors. He healed them and helped them as only He could.

Before long, it was past dinnertime. It would be dark soon. The disciples worried. It was a huge crowd, and the people were growing hungry. What would they find to eat?

One of Jesus' Disciples, Andrew, noticed in the crowd a boy who had five barley loaves and two fish.

Even though the boy knew it wasn't enough to feed everyone, he offered his food to Andrew. It wasn't much, but he gave it anyway.

The people looked at the boy and his food. Five barley loaves and two fish for this big crowd would never be enough! How would this little bit of food do when there were so many hungry people?

Jesus said to His Disciples, "Help everyone find a place to sit."

Jesus took the bread that the boy had given. He lifted it to Heaven and said a blessing, thanking His Father for the bread. Then He broke the bread and gave it to His Disciples. The Disciples took the bread to the people, giving some to everyone.

Then Jesus took the fish the boy had given. He lifted it to Heaven and said a blessing, thanking His Father for the fish. He divided the fish and gave it to His Disciples. The Disciples took the fish to the people, again giving some to everyone.

The Disciples gave out more bread and more fish. Other people came, and the Disciples kept giving out more and more food. There was always enough. All of the people in the large crowd got plenty of food to eat.

209

After everyone had eaten, Jesus told the Disciples to gather up what was left. The Disciples gathered twelve baskets full of leftover bread.

Even with only five barley loaves and two fish, Jesus, the Son of God, made enough food for everyone—and He even made leftovers! Everyone was fed by God that day. It was a miracle!

Bible Lesson

Jesus performed many wonderful miracles that showed that He was the Son of God and that He loved people very much.

Discussion Questions

Why did Jesus continue to teach the people who came to see Him, even though He was very tired?

The boy gave Jesus all of the food he had. How do you share what you have when people are in need?

What was the miracle that Jesus performed? Do you know of any other of Jesus' miracles?

Two Parables:
The Good Samaritan and The Prodigal Son

Retold by
Megan Howard

Illustrated by
Philomena O'Neill

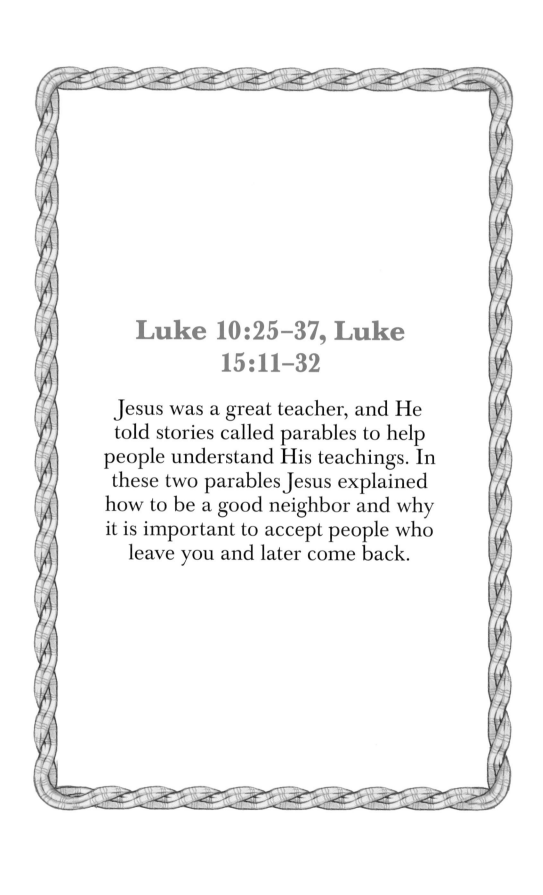

Luke 10:25–37, Luke 15:11–32

Jesus was a great teacher, and He told stories called parables to help people understand His teachings. In these two parables Jesus explained how to be a good neighbor and why it is important to accept people who leave you and later come back.

Many years ago, Jesus tried to help people understand the meaning and purpose of God's laws. To make the laws easier to understand, Jesus told stories called parables. Two of His most famous parables are the Good Samaritan and the Prodigal Son.

One day a crowd of followers surrounded Jesus. A man spoke up. "How do I get into Heaven?" he wanted to know.

"What does the law tell you?" Jesus asked.

"To love God with all your heart and mind and to love your neighbor as you love yourself," he said. "But who is my neighbor?"

To answer the man's question, Jesus told the
crowd the story of the Good Samaritan.

"A man was walking from Jerusalem to
Jericho," He began. The man met some robbers.
They beat him and took everything he had. They
ran away and left him badly hurt by the side of
the road.

A priest came down the road and saw the man. He didn't know who the man was or where he was from, so he didn't stop to help him. He crossed the street and kept walking.

Next a Levite came down the road and saw the man. He also didn't know who the man was or where he was from. Like the priest, he crossed the street and walked away without stopping to help.

Soon a Samaritan came down the road and saw the man lying on the ground. Even though he knew nothing about the man, the Samaritan could see that he was hurt and needed help. He stopped to care for the man. He washed him and cleaned his wounds.

The Samaritan put the injured man on his own donkey and took him to an inn. When he had to leave, the Samaritan gave the innkeeper some coins.

"Please take care of this man," he said. "If this isn't enough money, I'll give you more when I return."

When he finished the story, Jesus looked at the man in the crowd. "Who was the hurt man's neighbor?"

"The Samaritan was his neighbor," the man answered. "Even though he didn't know the injured man, he helped him."

Jesus nodded. "Go and do as he did."

Another time, Jesus' followers were upset with Him. They whispered to one another because they didn't understand why He was kind to sinners. To explain why, Jesus told them the story of the Prodigal Son.

A man had two sons. These brothers knew that someday everything their father owned would be divided between them. The younger brother couldn't wait. One day he asked for his share. The father divided his property and gave each son his part.

The younger son took what he got and left home. Instead of working, this son was prodigal— he spent his money every which way. He did whatever made him happy, and he was never bored.

Before long, all of his money
was gone. Famine hit the country,
so there wasn't enough for people to
eat. The son was hungry all of the time.

He asked a landowner he knew for help. The landowner gave him a job working on his pig farm. The pigs had plenty to eat. The son would have been happy with their food, but he got nothing.

The son remembered how well his father's workers ate. "Why am I here starving?" he thought. "If I worked as my father's servant, at least I could eat."

He decided to return home.

As the younger son walked up the path toward their house, his father saw him. The old man ran to hug him.

"I no longer deserve to be called your son," the young man said. He asked if he could become one of his father's workers.

Instead the father called his servants. He told them to put his own best robe and sandals on his son. They placed a ring on his finger.

"We will have a special meal!" the father announced. "Prepare the fattened calf."

The older son had been working in his father's field. As he walked toward the house, he heard the party that was going on inside. He asked a servant why everyone was celebrating.

"Your brother is back," the servant explained. The older brother got mad and refused to go into the house.

When his father saw the older son standing outside, he went to him. He asked his son to join the celebration.

"I never disobeyed you and worked very hard for you," the angry son said. "You never gave me a special meal to share with my friends!"

"We have always been together," the father said. "Everything I have is yours. But your brother was gone, and now he's come back to us. We must celebrate!"

After he finished the parable, Jesus explained that sinners were like the younger son. He celebrated their return for the same reason the father in the story welcomed his son. Jesus was happy when they came back to Him.

Bible Lesson

Jesus told stories called parables to help people understand God's laws. In the parable of The Good Samaritan, Jesus explained that we should love our neighbor as we love ourselves. Jesus told the parable of The Prodigal Son to teach that God will forgive us for our sins if we are truly sorry, and that we should forgive other people in the same way.

Discussion Questions

What does it mean to love your neighbor as yourself? How do you show kindness for others? How do you show kindness for people that you don't know well or that you may not like?

What does it mean to be prodigal? Talk about how the two brothers were different in how they behaved.

Why did the prodigal son's father forgive him? Why should we forgive people when they're sorry for what they've done?

Old Testament
Discussion Questions

How do the *Noah's Ark* and *David and Goliath* stories show how God helps you through difficult situations?

How did God help people get through scary times? How did He help Noah? Jonah? Daniel?

Adam and Eve and Jonah didn't obey God. What happened in each of those stories as a result?

How does God respond to those who are faithful to Him? Discuss Noah and Daniel.

The tenth commandment tells us that you shouldn't be jealous of other people. In the stories, what people were jealous? Discuss Joseph's brothers and King Darius's advisors.

Are there any other commandments that were broken in any of the stories?

There are many kings in these stories. Think about the relationship that Pharoah, King Saul, and King Darius had with Joseph, David, and Daniel. How did the kings come to know and trust these men?

New Testament Discussion Questions

People often refer to the New Testament as "Good News." Think about the life of Jesus, starting with His birth, and talk about how He brings good news to people.

Talk about the miracles of Jesus, such as when He fed thousands of people with five loaves and two fish and when He walked on water. Why did Jesus perform miracles? What do you think it would be like to see a miracle?

Jesus used parables to teach people. Talk about other ways in which He was a good teacher.

With the parable of *The Good Samaritan*, Jesus showed how He wanted people to love and care for one another. What ways in the stories did people love and care for one another?

Talk about the ways in which Jesus helped people who have worry or doubt.

What are the ways in which Jesus showed His love for people?

In *Five Loaves and Two Fish*, Jesus thanked God for the food and then was able to feed thousands of people. Why is giving thanks important? What are things that the people in the stories should be thankful for?

Glossary

advisor–*a person who offers advice and opinions*

ark–*a huge boat*

casting lots–*a way of making decisions by throwing sticks or pebbles*

commandment–*one of God's rules*

covet–*to want something that belongs to someone else*

cup bearer–*a person that serves wine in the king's household*

Disciples–*twelve followers of Jesus who believed in Him and helped to spread His teachings*

disobey–*to fail to follow a rule*

famine–*a severe shortage of food*

goblet–*a drinking cup that has a base and stem*

guardian angel–*an angel sent by God to protect someone*

Israelites–*those regarded as the chosen people of God*

Levite–*a Temple worker*

manger–*a stall used to feed cattle*

miracle–*an amazing act of God*

parable–*a story told by Jesus to help people understand the word of God*

Philistines–*people from ancient Philistia, often considered barbaric*

prodigal–*wasteful*

prophet–*a person who is chosen by God to tell His message*

repent–*to stop bad behavior completely and then change for the better*

Sabbath–*the seventh day of the week, a day of rest*

Samaritan–*a person from Samaria*

Savior–*Jesus Christ, the Son of God, who will deliver people from evil*

Acknowledgments

Hooked on Phonics Team

President
Christopher Paucek

VP, Product Development and Education
Wendy Paige Bronfin

Directors of Product Development and Education
Michael Artin
Russell Ginns

Editorial Director
Dorothy M. Taguchi, Ph.D.

Art Director
Russell Zambito

Producer
Amy Kraft

Production Assistant
Ryan McFarland

Educational Team

Nan Brall
Lynn Bain

Cover Design

William Fox Munroe, Inc.

Graphic Design

Eleanor Shelton

Print Production

Big Yellow Taxi, Inc.
SunDried Penguin

Special Thanks to
Leslie Alacbay, Jennifer Alvarez, Marsha Frank Berke, Keith Dix,
Lynette Fletcher, Rault Kehlor, Cathy Magbee, Mark Mashaw,
Lorrin Ortiz, Wynter Towns, and Troy Schremmer.